EARLY PHONICS IN CONTEXT

Written by Bev Heaton

World Teachers Press

Order Number 2-5035
ISBN 1-885111-48-7

E F   01 02 03

Educational Resources

395 Main Street
Rowley, MA 01969

Introduction

In *Early Phonics In Context,* each phonic sound is introduced in context, allowing students to identify the specific sound within text. Thus, students will be able to process automatically each phonic sound for pronunciation and meaning, thereby enhancing their reading and spelling skills. The activities in the book also provide reinforcement of each sound, and the comprehension stories which follow enable the students to identify the sounds in context.

Magic e
whiners
2V6W
Crazy R

Contents

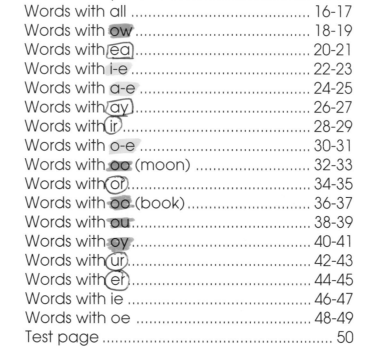

Teacher Information

Introduction

The teaching of basic sounds has long been recognized as an important component when learning the English language. This series of books looks at introducing the digraph sounds that form the foundation of this learning, through a variety of interesting and fun activities which students will enjoy. In addition, the author has provided activities that include the specific digraph sound in the context of a short story. This 'learning in context' is a vital part of learning and is a feature of this series. The activities are the product of many years of practice and application by the author and represent a wealth of experience.

What is a digraph?

A digraph is formed when a pair of letters make a single sound, such as *ew* in *stew* or *th* in *thief.*

It is important to teach digraphs and trigraphs as part of a language program. It provides students with a background in graphophonics and enables them to recognize letter patterns in their reading, writing and oral language.

As an extension, it is also important to teach that some letter combinations form different sound patterns in different situations such as *th* in *thief* and *th* in *then.* It is also necessary to teach students that the same sounds can be formed using different letter combinations such as, *ar* in *jar* and *au* in *aunt.*

Development

Below are two activities which could also be incorporated to develop the children's awareness of visual patterns and letter combinations.

1. Ask students to make pairs of words that rhyme, e.g. mouse/house. This could be developed further as a game of *Snap* or *Patience.*

2. Use the game *Hangman* with an alternative rule. The students must give you letters of the word in the correct order. The letters selected by the students will fit into three areas.

   (i) Could be - these are letter combinations that belong together (e.g. ye).

   (ii) Couldn't be - these are letter combinations that don't belong together (e.g. yt).

   (iii) The letter is the next letter in the word and is placed as part of the secret word.

Teacher Information - example lesson development

The following is a lesson development using one of the pages in this book. It is an example of how the activity could be introduced, developed and extended.

Activity   'ee' as in creek - pages 6 & 7

Introductory Work   Introducing a sound can be done in a variety of ways. However the two most important parts of the introduction should be first, to identify places or words where the sound can be found. This then gives the students a logical reason to learn the sound and hence the words containing this sound. Secondly, the correct pronunciation of the sound is important so that different sounds can be easily distinguished. Students can contribute to both of these areas and a large group activity suits these items well.

Pictures representing words containing the 'ee' sound will assist with the introduction.

Development   The first worksheet identifies the sound and allows the students to practice using the sound to make different words, using pictorial clues.

The second worksheet provides a passage of writing which includes a quantity of 'ee' words. This will allow the students to work the 'ee' words in context and gain a greater level of understanding.

1. First activity provides practice in creating 'ee' words by tracing over the 'ee' sound. Students should verbalize their answers wherever possible.

2. Matching the correct word to the picture will ensure that the word is understood.

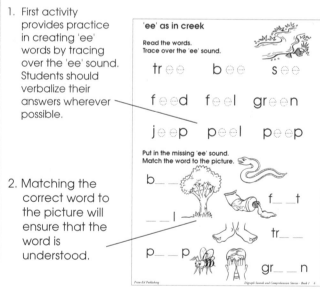

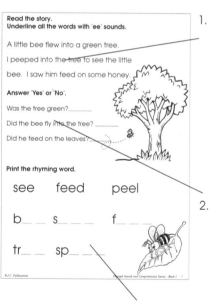

3. Follow up by identifying more 'ee' words and writing them on the board for students to practice.

1. Read the story as a class, with students following the words. Talk about what happened in the story.

2. Ask the questions and then have students write their answers.

3. Complete the 'ee' words.

Extension   Further use of digraph sounds and words containing these sounds should become part of the daily language program. Where words containing these sounds are located they should be identified and discussed to further emphasize the sound in the context of the student's daily contact with written language.

'ee' as in creek

Read the words.
Trace over the 'ee' sound.

tr e e   b e e   s e e

f e d   f e l   gr e e n

j e p   p e e l   p e e p

Put in the missing 'ee' sound.
Match the word to the picture.

b __ __

f __ __ t

__ __ l

tr __ __ __

p __ __ p

gr __ __ n

Early Phonics In Context *World Teachers Press*

Read the story.
Underline all the words with 'ee' sounds.

A little bee flew into a green tree.

I peeped into the tree to see the little

bee. I saw it feed on some honey.

Answer 'Yes' or 'No'.

Was the tree green?_____

Did the bee fly into the tree? _____

Did he feed on the leaves?_____

Print the rhyming word.

see   feed   peel

b__ __   s__ __ __   f__ __ __

tr__ __   sp__ __ __

'ar' as in car

Trace over the dotted 'ar' sound.

c ar   st ar   f ar

st art   f arm

c ard   h ard

Print the missing 'ar' sound.
Match the word to the picture.

c __ __

c __ __ d

st __ __

f __ __ m

How many 'ar' words are on this page? _____

Read the story.
Circle all the 'ar' sounds.

The farm was far, far away. The car would not start.

Jack pushed the car but it was too hard.

The farmer came and started the car.

Jack and the farmer

drove to the farm.

Fill in the missing words.

The farm was _____, _____ away. The

_____ would not _____. Jack pushed

the _____ but it would not _____.

Answer these questions.

What was far away?

_____

Who pushed the car?

_____

Why do you think the car would not start?

_____

'ai' as in train

Read the words.
Trace over the 'ai' sounds.

chain   train

   tail   pail

rail   mail

   sail   pain

Put in the missing 'ai' sound.
Match the word to the picture.

r _ _ n

p _ _ nt

s _ _ l

t _ _ l

Read the story.
Circle all the 'ai' sounds.

The train was in the rain. The paint came off the

train. We put some red paint

in the pail and painted the

train. The train is back on

the rails.

Put in the missing words.

The _____ was in the _____. The _____

came off the _____. We put some red _____

in the _____ and _____ the _____.

The _____ is back on the _____.

Answer 'Yes' or 'No'.

Can you paint a train?_____

Was the train in the rain?_____

Was the paint in the pail?_____

Was the paint blue?_____

'oa' as in boat

Trace over the 'oa' sound.

b o a t   g o a t   c o a t

s o a k   gr o a n

cr o a k   m o a n

Print the missing 'oa' sound.
Match the word to the picture.

c __ __ t

croak

b __ __ t

cr __ __ k

g __ __ t

Read the story.
Underline all the words with 'oa' sounds.

The little goat wore a red coat. He

got into a boat with a frog.

The frog went 'croak croak'.

Answer these questions.

Who wore the red coat?

_____

What did the goat get into?

_____

What did the frog say?

_____

_____

Read and draw.

A goat wearing a red coat in a boat.

Early Phonics In Context

'y' as in sunny

Read the words.
Trace over the 'y' sound.

funny   happy

sticky   jolly   hurry

sunny   sorry

Print the missing 'y' sound.
Match the word to the picture.

cand__   pupp__

jell__   cherr__

bunn__   doll__

Early Phonics In Context   *World Teachers Press*

Read the story.
Circle all the 'y' sounds.

A funny jolly bunny made a cherry jelly.
The jelly was tasty. Bunny gave the
jelly to the puppy. The puppy was
very happy.

Answer these questions.

Who was jolly?

_____

What was tasty?

_____

Who did bunny give the jelly to? **Read and draw.**

_____

_____

_____

Why was the puppy happy?

_____

_____

_____

A jolly bunny with the puppy.

'all' as in ball

Print the missing 'all' sound.

w_____   t_____

b_____   sm_____

c_____   f_____

Trace over the 'all' sound.
Match the word to the picture.

 sm a l l

 b a l l   w a l l

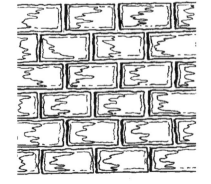

c a l l

Read the story.
Circle the 'all' sounds.

Once upon a time there lived a small ant.

He crawled up a tall wall. When he reached

the top of the wall he called out. The small

ant had a fall, he fell off the wall.

Answer 'Yes' or 'No'.

Was the ant small? _____

Did the ant jump off the wall? _____

Did the ant reach the top of the wall?_____

Did the ant fall off the wall?_____

Rhyming words.

ball   c_ _ _   f_ _ _

t_ _ _   h_ _ _

Answer these questions.
Who was small?

_____

What did the ant climb up?

_____

'ow' as in cow

Trace over the 'ow' sound.

n ow   h ow

         cl ow n

br ow n   t ow n

        c ow

Print the missing 'ow' sound.
Match the word to the picture.

cl __ __ n

c __ __

fr __ __ n

cr __ __ n

      Early Phonics In Context   *World Teachers Press*

Read the story.
Underline all the words with 'ow' sounds.

One day a brown cow went to town to see if

she could find a clown with a frown. The brown

cow did not find the clown with a

frown. She found an owl.

Fill in the missing words.

One day a _____ _____ went to

_____ to see if she could find a _____

with a _____. She found an _____.

Answer these questions.

Who went to town?

_____

What was she looking for?   **Read and draw.**

_____

_____

_____

What did she find?

_____

_____   A brown cow sitting near a
                                          clown and owl.

'ea' as in leaf

Read the words.
Trace over the 'ea' sound.

s e a   l e a k   b e a ch

b e a k   r e a d   m e a t

cl e a n   str e a m

Put in the missing 'ea' sound.
Match the word to the picture.

s__ __t   l__ __f

t__ __   p__ __ch

p__ __   s__ __l

Read the story.
Circle all the 'ea' sounds.

Sammy Seal lived in the sea. He sat on the clean

beach and ate a pea and a peach.

Sammy Seal loved the peach.

Answer these questions.
Who lived by the sea?

_____

Where did he sit?

_____

What did Sammy Seal eat?

_____

Do you think he enjoyed the peach?_____

Why?_____

Read and draw.

```
Sammy Seal sitting on the beach eating a peach.
```

'i-e' as in bike

Read the words.
Trace over the 'i-e' sound.

bike   pipe   ride

slide   like

pine   hive   dive

Print the missing 'i-e' sound.
Match the word to the picture.

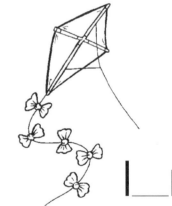

k_t_   l_n_

sm_l_   f_v_

t_m_   r_d_

Read the story.
Circle all the 'i-e' sounds.

It was time for the bees to make their hives.

The bees made five hives. The hives were in a pine

tree. A pipe and a slide were near the hives.

A kite was in the tree. The students could not play

near the tree.

Answer these questions.

What did the bees make?

_____

How many hives did the bees make?

_____

What was near the hives?

_____

Why couldn't the students play near the tree?

_____

Rhyming words.

bike   h___ ___ ___   sp___ ___ ___

'a-e' as in cake

Read the words.
Trace over the 'a-e' sound.

c a v e   g a t e   c a k e

wh a l e   sp a d e

s a m e   g a m e

Print the missing 'a-e' sound.
Match the word to the picture.

w_v_   pl_n_

gr_p_   l_k_

sn_k_   c_k_

Read the story.
Underline all the words with 'a-e' sounds.

Gaye had a birthday party.

She had a cake and some toy snakes.

She got a spade and a whale balloon.

Gaye waved goodbye to her friends.

Answer 'Yes' or 'No'.

Did Gaye have a birthday? _____

Did Gaye get a spade?_____

Did Gaye wave goodbye? _____

Print the missing words.

_____ had a party. She had a

_____ and some toy _____.

She got a _____ and a _____ balloon.

'ay' as in tray

Trace over the 'ay' sound.

say   tray

   day   bay

stay   May

  away   hay

Print the missing 'ay' sound.
Match the word to the picture.

tr＿＿

b＿＿   h＿＿

s＿＿    pr＿＿

Read the story.
Underline all the words with 'ay' sounds.

One day in the middle of May, two little

boys went to stay with their friends. Their

friends lived near a bay. In the bay swam

lots of fish. The boys said they would

stay all day until they caught some fish.

The boys didn't catch any fish.

Rhyming words.

May   st____ ____   b____ ____   tr____ ____   h____ ____

Answer 'Yes' or 'No'.

Did the two boys stay
with their friends?

_____

Were there lots of fish
in the bay?

_____

Did the boys catch
any fish?

_____

Read and draw.

Two boys standing in the bay, fishing.

'ir' as in bird

Print the missing 'ir' word.

g_ _l

th_ _d

b_ _d

d_ _t

sh_ _t

sk_ _t

Trace over the 'ir' sound.
Match the word to the picture.

bird

shirt

skirt

girl

Read the story.
Circle all the 'ir' sounds.

One morning a little girl went to play in the dirty

sand. She wore a shirt and a skirt. As she played

in the dirt a little bird flew down from the tree and

sat next to the little girl. He said 'Little girl, you will

get dirty if you sit in the dirt.' The little girl

did not hear the little bird.

Fill in the missing words.

A little _____ went to play in the sand.

A little _____ flew out of the tree.

Answer these questions.

What did the little girl wear?

_____

Where did the little girl play?

_____

Why did you think the bird spoke to the girl?

_____

'o-e' as in bone

Read the words.
Trace over the 'o-e' sounds.

clos e   p o k e   br o k e

sp o k e   h o m e   dr o v e

Put in the missing 'o-e' sound.
Match the word to the picture.

sl__p__  r__p__

h__m__  h__s__

b__n__   r__d__

 dr__v__

Read the story.
Underline the words with 'o-e' sound.

Scott rode home with a bone for Samson,

his dog. He put the bone near the hose

which was close to the rope.

Samson ate the bone.

Answer 'Yes' or 'No'.

Did Scott ride home?_____

Was the bone for Samson? _____

Did Scott put the bone near his home?_____

Did Scott eat the bone?_____

Answer these questions.
Who rode home?

_____

Why did Scott ride home?

_____

Who ate the bone?

_____

Why did Samson eat the bone?

_____

'oo' as in moon

Read the words.
Trace over the 'oo' sound.

r o o m   r o o f   d r o o p

b o o t   f o o d   z o o m

Put in the missing 'oo' sound.
Match the word to the picture.

br_ _m      z_ _

sp_ _n   h_ _p

m_ _n   t_ _th

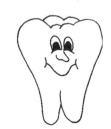

Read the story.
Underline all the words with 'oo' sounds.

In the room, there was a broom, a boot,

a hoop and a spoon. There was no food.

Above the roof, the moon shone. It did

not shine at noon.

Answer these questions.

Was there food in the room?_____

What was above the roof?_____

What was in the room?_____

Print the rhyming word.

room   hoop   moon

z_ _ _   dr_ _ _   sp_ _ _

br_ _ _   l_ _ _   n_ _ _

'or' as in fork

Print the missing 'or' sound.

c_ _k   f_ _k

c_ _n

t_ _n   b_ _n

Trace over the 'or' sound.
Match the word to the picture.

c o r n      t o r n

f o r k   c o r k

Read the story.
Circle all the 'or' sounds.

Farmer Jack grew corn. He picked the corn in the morning. He put the corn into a torn bag. The corn was sold that morning.

Fill in the missing words.

Farmer Jack grew _____.

He picked the _____

in the _____. He put the _____

into a _____ bag.

Answer these questions.

What did Farmer Jack grow?

_____

When did he pick the corn?

_____

Why do you think he picked the corn in the morning?

_____

_____

'oo' as in book

Trace over the dotted 'oo' sound.

b o o k   l o o k

g o o d   t o o k

c o o k   br o o k

Print the missing 'oo' sound.
Match the word to the picture.

b_ _k

c_ _ _k

br_ _ _k   t_ _ _k

Read the story.
Circle all the 'oo' sounds.

The good cook stood by a stove to cook.

It took him a long time to look through

the cookbook. It took him a

long time to cook.

Answer 'Yes' or 'No'.

Was the cook a good cook? _____

Did it take him a long time to cook? _____

Was the cook a girl? _____

Did the cook stand on a chair? _____

Rhyming words.

cook

b__ __ __

t__ __ __

l__ __ __

sh__ __ __

Read and draw.

A cook with a book.

'ou' as in house

Print the missing 'ou' sound.
Match the word to the picture.

m__ __se

p__ __ch

sh__ __t

cl__ __d

r__ __nd

h__ __se

Print the missing word.

mouse   house   pouch

A kangaroo has a large _____.

round   shout   cloud

A dark _____ was in the sky.

Read the story.
Underline all the words with 'ou' sounds.

One day a small gray mouse ran through my house. My mother saw the mouse and shouted out loud. The little joey standing outside got frightened and jumped into her mother's pouch. Once inside her pouch the joey turned round and peeped out to see what
had frightened her. She
saw a little gray mouse
running through the house.

Answer these questions.

Who ran through the house?

_____

Why do you think the mouse ran through the house?

_____

Why did the joey get frightened?

_____

Do you think the mouse was frightened? _____

Why? _____

How many 'ou' words did you find? _____

'oy' as in boy

Print the missing 'oy' sound.
Match the word to the picture.

t__ __

b__ __

j__ __

Tr__ __

ann__ __

ah__ __

R__ __

AHOY!

Answer Yes/No.

Is Roy a boy? _____

Can you play with a toy? _____

Do you enjoy ice cream? _____

Have you tasted an oyster? _____

Early Phonics In Context

Read the story.
Circle all the words with 'oy' sounds.

Troy and Roy went to the beach. They took their toy shovels and buckets. Roy also took his toy boat. As Troy and Roy played on the rocks they saw an oyster. Troy tried to pick the oyster off with Roy's toy shovel but the shovel broke. Roy was very annoyed. Troy did not get the oyster.

Answer these questions.

Who went to the beach?

_____

What did they take with them?

_____

What was under a rock?

_____

Who broke the shovel?

_____

Why was Roy annoyed? _____

_____

How many 'oy' words did you find? _____

'ur' as in church

Finish the words.
Draw a picture for each word.

b __ __ st

f __ __ __

t __ __ nip

h __ __ t

ch __ __ ch

c __ __ l

Print the missing words.

fur   **turnip**

The rabbit had soft _____.

burst   **hurt**

Rover _____ his leg on the sharp fence.

turnip   **church**

Jack grew a large _____ in his garden.

Read the story.
Circle all the words with 'ur' sounds.

Tommy Turtle went for a stroll one Thursday. Tommy walked and walked until he came to a church. His feet hurt, so he sat near some turnips, which were next to the church. He curled up and went to sleep. He did not wake up until Saturday.

Answer these questions.

What was the turtle's name?

_____

Where did Tommy walk to?

_____

What did he sit near?

_____

How do you think the turtle felt?

_____

_____

For how many days did Tommy sleep? _____

How many 'ur' words did you find? _____

'er' as in fern

Finish the words.
Draw a picture for each word.

f __ __ n

h __ __

h __ __ d

riv __ __

tig __ __

ladd __ __

Print the missing words.

fern   **perch**

A little bird has a _____ in his cage.

her   **fern**

A green _____ grows in my garden.

ladder   **panther**

A _____ is a wild animal.

Read the story.
Underline all the words with 'er' sounds.

In the garden grew some lovely ferns and some very pretty flowers. The ferns grew very tall and a ladder was needed to reach the top of the tallest ferns. A stone panther sat among the flowers. A river flowed along the side of the fern garden. A bird was perched high in a tree, singing sweetly. The garden was always perfect.

Answer these questions.

What grew in the garden?

_____

What grew very tall? _____

What animal sat among the flowers?

_____

Why do you think the garden was perfect?

_____

Why do you think the bird sang sweetly?

_____

How many 'er' words did you find?

_____

'ie' as in die

Print the missing 'ie' sound.
Match the word to the picture.

l_ _

t_ _

p_ _

d_ _

Singular and plural.
Add 's' to make them more than one.

pie_   p_ _ _

tie_   t_ _ _

lie_   l_ _ _

Put the missing words.

Ben wore a _____ around his neck.

Pets will _____ if you don't feed them.

I like ice cream with my _____.